# The WILD Thornberrys™

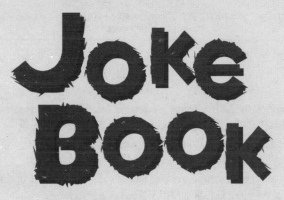

# Joke Book

KLASKY
CSUPO INC.

Based on the TV series *The Wild Thornberrys*® created by Klasky Csupo, Inc.,
as seen on Nickelodeon®

ISBN  0-439-28334-5

12 11 10 9 8 7 6 5 4 3 2 1                 1 2 3 4 5 6/0

Printed in the U.S.A.
First Scholastic printing, May 2001

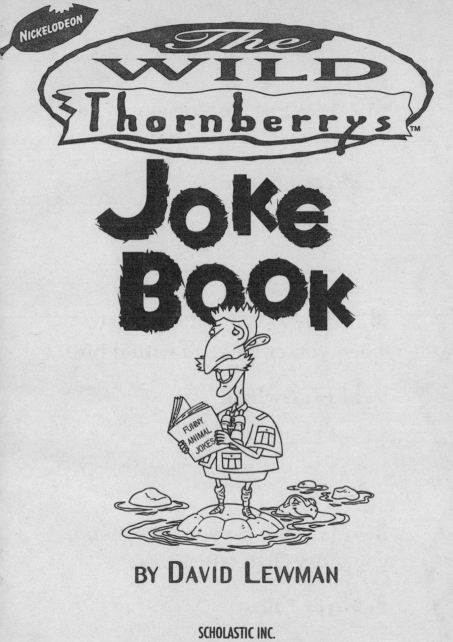

# The WILD Thornberrys™

# JOKE BOOK

FUNNY ANIMAL JOKES

NICKELODEON

## BY DAVID LEWMAN

### SCHOLASTIC INC.

New York   Toronto   London   Auckland   Sydney
Mexico City   New Delhi   Hong Kong

**Nigel:** What do you get when you cross Eliza with a reptile?

**Debbie:** Elizard!

**Marianne:** What do you get when you cross Eliza with a bird?

**Debbie:** Owliza!

**Nigel:** What do you get when you cross Eliza with a fish?

**Debbie:** Eeliza!

**Debbie:** What do you call your best friend when he beats you at a game?

**Eliza:** Darwinner!

# Are the Thornberrys smart?

Yes, they're very sharp.

**Eliza:** Why is Mom filming that native bread?

**Nigel:** She needs some wild-loaf footage.

**Marianne:** How does Donnie like traveling with us?

**Eliza:** He's wild about it.

**Darwin:** What kind of insect has long blonde hair and reads *Teenage Wasteland?*

**Eliza:** A Deb-bee.

**Eliza:** What has red hair and goes great on toast?

**Darwin:** Nigelly!

**Eliza:** What do you get when you cross my mom with a tiny insect?

**Darwin:** A Mari-ant.

**Eliza:** What do you get when you cross Donnie with an old elephant?

**Debbie:** A mastodonnie.

**Eliza:** What do you call our camper when it turns too fast?

**Darwin:** The Commveer.

**Eliza:** Knock, knock.

**Darwin:** Who's there?

**Eliza:** Skip.

**Darwin:** Skip who?

**Eliza:** 'S Kip O'Donnell—run!


**Marianne:** What did Nigel say when the elephant stepped on the coconut?

**Debbie:** "Smashing!"


**Debbie:** What would you call Kip's sidekick if he were a bug?

**Eliza:** Beetleman.

**Darwin:** What would you sing if you saw Biederman's partner raising animals in the country?

**Eliza:** "Kip O'Donnell had a farm, E, I, E, I, O . . ."

**Darwin:** Why is Nigel so interested in wildlife?

**Eliza:** It's just his nature.

**Eliza:** Why did Donnie push Mom's film equipment down the mountain?

**Nigel:** He wanted to roll the cameras.

**Eliza:** What did the film say to the camera?

**Darwin:** "Look at me—I'm on a roll!"

**Darwin:** What's Nigel's favorite constellation?

**Eliza:** The Big Kipper.

**Nigel:** Knock, knock.

**Debbie:** Who's there?

**Nigel:** Saul.

**Debbie:** Saul who?

**Nigel:** Salty kippers—yum!

**Darwin:** How long has Donnie been wild?

**Eliza:** Since the day he was Borneo.

**Eliza:** What'll happen to Darwin if he eats too many of his favorite treats?

**Nigel:** He'll turn into a chimpancheesy.

**Nigel:** How did Eliza feel after eating too much of her favorite pudding?

**Marianne:** Plum tuckered out.

What did Eliza sing when she heard something ringing in the Amazon?

"Jungle bells, jungle bells, jungle all the way..."

**How have the Thornberrys' trips to Africa gone?**

Safari, so good.

**Debbie:** Who sells the wettest flowers in South America?

**Marianne:** The rain florist.

**Eliza:** Which woods are the smartest?

**Darwin:** The brain forest.

**Eliza:** Which woods are full of kings and queens?

**Darwin:** The reign forest.

**Marianne:** What happened when the boy volcano met the girl volcano?

**Debbie:** It was lava at first sight.

Do Darwin and Eliza like to go up trees together?

Yes, they're partners-in-climb.

# What did Debbie say when Darwin fell out of the tree?

**"Better luck next climb."**

What do you call Eliza, Darwin, and Donnie when they climb trees together?

The Tree Musketeers.

**Eliza:** Which tree has the best food in it?

**Darwin:** The pantry.

**Eliza:** Which tree always stays warm?

**Darwin:** The fir tree.

**Eliza:** Which tree is always handy?

**Darwin:** The palm.

# Can Eliza talk to trees?

No, but she understands their bark.

**Eliza:** Why aren't trees good actors?

**Nigel:** They give wooden performances.

**Eliza:** Can you ride on a vine, Darwin?

**Darwin:** Yes, I think I can swing it.

# Why did Eliza and Darwin climb on vines?

They wanted to be in the swing of things.

# Is Darwin like his father?

Yes, he's a chimp off the old block.

What do you call Darwin covered in black and white stripes?

A chimpanzebra.

What do you call Darwin when he's eaten way too much?

A blimpanzee.

Eliza: Who's big, green, and hangs around in the jungle?

Debbie: Frankenvine.

 Which ape is the smallest?

The shrimpanzee.

**Eliza:** Knock, knock.

**Debbie:** Who's there?

**Eliza:** Annie.

**Debbie:** Annie who?

**Eliza:** Animals are my life!


**Debbie:** Where do creatures go shopping?

**Nigel:** The ani-mall.

**Debbie:** Knock, knock.

**Eliza:** Who's there?

**Debbie:** School.

**Eliza:** School who?

**Debbie:** 'S cool to be me, you know?

**Debbie:** How do you like my jeans, Dad?

**Nigel:** I think they're ripping!

What does Nigel call it when his daughters perform?

A poppet show.

Why are moutains smelly?

They're right next to the foothills.

What does Eliza say to a cat when she's hurt herself?

"Me-ow!"

How did Eliza do when she
tried to talk to mice?

She squeaked by.

Why did Eliza read a whole
book to the warthog?

She wanted
to make a long
story snort.

Why didn't Eliza tell
the wild boar her secrets?

She was afraid he'd squeal.

Did the wild boar have a stand-in for the Thornberrys' nature film?

No, he did all his own grunts.

**Darwin:** Why did Donnie race to the top of the tree?

**Eliza:** He wanted to be a runner-up.

What do you get when you cross a crocodile and a parrot?

A squawkodile.

**Nigel:** Why did Eliza put Donnie on her shoulders?

**Marianne:** She wanted to wear a jumper.

**Nigel:** Why does Donnie run in bed?

**Marianne:** Because he's fast asleep.

What did Debbie say when Eliza told her she saw a warthog in the forest?

"Wartever!"

What is Debbie's favorite fruit?

BOYSenberries.

Why did Debbie come to a screeching halt?

She saw a shop sign.

Eliza: What do you call a shopping center in the jungle?

Debbie: The Mall of the Wild.

# What does Debbie call it when Eliza dances with Darwin?

"Dancing geek-to-geek."

# What happened to Biederman's plan to set a trap with a covered pit?

It fell through.

# Why did Eliza say "excuse me" to the bird?

She chirped.

# Why didn't Eliza talk to the mountain goat behind the shrub?

She didn't want to bleat around the bush.

## What did Eliza ask the wild donkey's mother?

"Can your daughter come out and bray?"

## What did the horse tell Eliza after the race?

"You whinny some, you losey some."

## What did Eliza say to the horse?

"That's easy for you to neigh."

**Darwin:** What do you call a horse who's dull to talk to?

**Eliza:** A neigh-bore.

**Darwin:** Why are wolf sentences so hard to untangle?

**Eliza:** They're always snarled.


What do you call a cat who speaks like a parakeet?

A cheeping tom.


What do you call a parakeet who dresses up like a dog?

A cheep in wolf's clothing.

Why couldn't Eliza understand the duck?

He had a very strong quackcent.

Darwin: What do you call the geese's leader?

Eliza: A honker chief.

What did the frog say when he heard Eliza talk?

"The croak's on you."

How does Eliza talk to crows?

Cawtiously.

**What's it called when a crow makes a joke?**

Cawmedy.

**What were Eliza and the owl talking about?**

They were just hooting the breeze.

**Darwin:** Does that pigeon know how he lost his voice?

**Eliza:** He doesn't have a coo.

**How was the Thornberrys' show about desert animals?**

A little dry.

**Darwin:** What position did the crab play on the baseball team?

**Eliza:** Pinch critter.

**Eliza:** Why do desert animals always brag?

**Darwin:** They're full of hot air.

**What did Eliza say after she saw an avalanche?**

"That rocked!"

**Why did Marianne shoot the film during a sandstorm?**

She'd been saving it for a grainy day.

**Debbie:** What's the smelliest part of a movie?

**Marianne:** The footage.

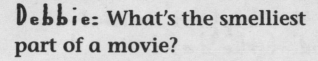

# Why did Nigel and Marianne film the biggest animal at the end of the day?

**They saved the beast for last.**